The Story
of The
Fourth Wise
Man

by
Sheila McCullagh

Pictures by
Rhian Nest James

When Jesus was born in Bethlehem, three wise men came to visit him. They had seen a great star in the east, and they set out from their homes to follow the star.

They followed the star for many days and nights, until at last they came to the stable in Bethlehem, and there they saw Jesus, with Mary and Joseph.

But there was also a fourth wise man who saw the star and followed it. This is the story of the fourth wise man.

The fourth wise man lived on the edge of the desert, towards Egypt. When he saw the great star in the east, he left his home and followed the star towards Bethlehem.

The fourth wise man was not as rich as the other wise men. He rode a donkey, and he travelled alone.

The fourth wise man travelled for seven days and nights, following the star.

On the eighth day, he saw a sheep which had gone over a cliff. He stopped to find the shepherd, and he helped him to rescue the sheep.

Then he went on his way, following the star.

He had travelled a long way, when he saw a man lying by the roadside. The man had been attacked by robbers, who had left him for dead.

But the man was alive.

The fourth wise man stopped. He helped the man climb on to the donkey. Then he walked beside the donkey, and took the man to the nearest inn.

It was a long way back, along the road he had come.

The fourth wise man went on. But now he hurried, because he had spent such a long time on the way.

He was travelling in a very
lonely place, when he saw two children by the road.
They were cold and hungry. They had been lost for days.

9

He gave the children food. Then he put them on his donkey, and set out to find their father and mother.

It was many days before, at last, he found them.

The fourth wise man left the children, and went on his way.

He hurried on, until at last he came to Bethlehem.

11

At last the fourth wise man came to the stable in Bethlehem – but the stable was empty.

"Mary and Joseph and the baby left three days ago," said the Innkeeper. "No one knows where they have gone."

So the fourth wise man travelled sadly back towards his own home.

As he came towards his house, his son ran out to meet him. The boy was so glad that his father was back.

"Has anything happened since I left?" asked the fourth wise man.

14

"Two travellers came last night, with a little baby," said the boy. "They were very tired. There was nowhere for them to stay, so they are staying with us."

The fourth wise man went in with his son –
and there were Mary and Joseph and the Christ Child,
inside the gates of his own home.